高个子缇娜

【美】唐娜·玛丽·麦瑞特◎著

【美】丽萨·伍德拉夫◎绘

范晓星◎译

天津出版传媒集团

新蕾出版社

迈克尔、布利安娜和克里斯汀，感谢你们的鼓励，让我有种小巨人般的感觉。

——唐娜·玛丽·麦瑞特

图书在版编目（CIP）数据

高个子缇娜/(美)麦瑞特(Merritt,D.M.)著；
(美)伍德拉夫(Woodruff,L.)绘；范晓星译.-- 天津：
新蕾出版社,2015.12(2024.12重印)
(数学帮帮忙·互动版)
书名原文：Too-Tall Tina
ISBN 978-7-5307-6315-5

Ⅰ.①高… Ⅱ.①麦… ②伍… ③范… Ⅲ.①数学–
儿童读物 Ⅳ.①O1-49

中国版本图书馆 CIP 数据核字(2015)第 262656 号

Too-Tall Tina by Donna Marie Merritt; illustrated by Liza Woodruff. Copyright©
2005 by Kane Press, Inc. All rights reserved, including the right of reproduction in
whole or in part in any form. This edition published by arrangement with Kane
Press, Inc. New York, NY, represented by The ChoiceMaker Korea Co. Simplified
Chinese translation copyright © 2015 by New Buds Publishing House (Tianjin)
Limited Company
ALL RIGHTS RESERVED
本书中文简体版专有出版权经由中华版权代理中心授予新蕾出版社(天津)有
限公司。未经许可,不得以任何方式复制或抄袭本书的任何部分。
津图登字：02-2015-218

出版发行：天津出版传媒集团
　　　　　新蕾出版社
http://www.newbuds.com.cn
地　　址：天津市和平区西康路 35 号(300051)
出 版 人：马玉秀
电　　话：总编办 (022)23332422
　　　　　发行部 (022)23332679　23332351
传　　真：(022)23332422
经　　销：全国新华书店
印　　刷：天津新华印务有限公司
开　　本：787mm×1092mm　1/16
印　　张：3
版　　次：2015 年 12 月第 1 版　2024 年 12 月第 21 次印刷
定　　价：12.00 元

无处不在的数学

资深编辑　卢　江

　　人们常说"兴趣是最好的老师",有了兴趣,学习就会变得轻松愉快。数学对于孩子来说或许有些难,因为比起语文,数学显得枯燥、抽象,不容易理解,孩子往往不那么喜欢。可许多家长都知道,学数学对于孩子的成长和今后的生活有多么重要。不仅数学知识很有用,学习数学过程中获得的数学思想和方法更会影响孩子的一生,因为数学素养是构成人基本素质的一个重要因素。但是,怎样才能让孩子对数学产生兴趣呢?怎样才能激发他们兴致勃勃地去探索数学问题呢?我认为,让孩子读些有趣的书或许是不错的选择。读了这套"数学帮帮忙",我立刻产生了想把它们推荐给教师和家长朋友们的愿望,因为这真是一套会让孩子爱上数学的好书!

　　这套有趣的图书从美国引进,原出版者是美国资深教育专家。每本书讲述一个孩子们生活中的故事,由故事中出现的问题自然地引入一个数学知识,然后通过运用数学知识解决问题。比如,从帮助外婆整理散落的纽扣引出分类,从为小狗记录藏骨头的地点引出空间方位等等。故事素材全部来源于孩子们的真实生活，不是童话，不是幻想，而是鲜活的生活实例。正是这些发生在孩子身边的故事，让孩子们懂得，数学无处不在并且非常有用；这些鲜活的实例也使得抽象的概念更易于理解，更容易激发孩子学习数学的兴趣，让他们逐渐爱上数学。这样的教育思想和方法与我国近年来提倡的数学教育理念是十分吻合的！

这是一套适合5~8岁孩子阅读的书，书中的有趣情节和生动的插画可以将抽象的数学问题直观化、形象化，为孩子的思维活动提供具体形象的支持。如果亲子共读的话，家长可以带领孩子推测情节的发展，探讨解决难题的办法，让孩子在愉悦的氛围中学到知识和方法。

值得教师和家长朋友们注意的是，在每本书的后面，出版者还加入了"互动课堂"及"互动练习"，一方面通过一些精心设计的活动让孩子巩固新学到的数学知识，进一步体会知识的含义和实际应用；另一方面帮助家长指导孩子阅读，体会故事中数学之外的道理，逐步提升孩子的阅读理解能力。

我相信孩子读过这套书后一定会明白，原来，数学不是烦恼，不是包袱，数学真能帮大忙！

今年夏天，我的身体发生了奇妙的变化。
我长个儿了！越长越高，越长越高！

我去泰莎医生那里检查身体。"哇！缇娜！"她惊喜地说，"你真是长高了不少呢！"

我特自豪！

可上学第一天，我就没那么开心了。

　　以前,我和两个好朋友一样高。可现在,我比南希高了大半头,比卢克也高了一大截儿。我成了三年级个子最高的小孩儿!

高　　　更高　　　最高

我跟麦克打招呼。

"嗨,缇娜!"他一边回答,一边上下打量着我,
"哇! 我想说,哪儿来的傻大个儿!"

"上面的空气如何呀?"安娜也故意这样问我。

然后,他们两个人一起大笑起来。

我觉得一点儿都不好笑。

课间的时候，我找到了上学期我最喜欢的跳绳。这根跳绳是紫色的，手柄闪闪发光。我拿起便跳。扑通！跳绳变短了！这可是我最喜欢的跳绳啊！

也许麦克说得对，我真成傻大个了儿。

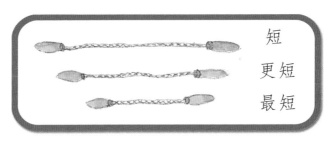

短

更短

最短

南希和卢克把我扶起来。

"谢谢。"我嘟囔道。

"别担心，"卢克说，"再去找根长一点儿的跳绳就好了！"

我想笑，可怎么也笑不出来。

终于要放学了。

"别忘了,星期五我们要拍集体照。"李老师提醒大家,"我们要拍出全校最帅的照片。"

同学们都兴奋极了,除了我。

为我们拍照的摄影师总是按个子高矮给大家安排位置。每年，我都和南希、卢克站在一起。

可是，今年不行了。

三年级

"我不想站在最后一排，离你们那么远。"我难过
地说。

"说不定你会喜欢站在最后一排呢！"南希安慰
我。

"就是！站在最后一排，没人会看出来你的袜子是
不是脏了！"卢克加上一句。

"可我们仨形影不离呀！我们是'三剑客'。"我回
答。

南希和卢克也郁闷地耸耸肩膀。

那天晚上，我想啊想……

有了！我有主意了。我来到衣橱，找了又找，终于……找到了！正合适！集体照那天南希和卢克能跟我一样高了。

上课前，我把这个主意告诉了卢克和南希。

"穿女生的鞋？"卢克吃惊地说，"不行！不行！"

"哦，高跟鞋呀！"南希穿上高跟鞋，试着走了几步。

摇摇晃晃，扑通！她摔了个大跟头。
方案一失败。

13

不过，我还有方案二。

我缩起脖子，微微弯曲膝盖，驼着背朝卢克走去。

"瞧，我跟你一样高了！"

"是呀，"卢克说，"可是你这样像只笨鸭子。"

唉，这可不太好。我只好站直了身子。

"嘿,同学们!"费利克斯大声喊,"谁想玩钻竹竿?"

"来了!来了!"南希和卢克应声跑过去。我也慢慢腾腾地跟了过去。

去年,我可是玩钻竹竿的高手。我能一直向后仰着身钻过竹竿,哪怕竹竿降到最低也没有问题。

可现在呢,我变成高个子缇娜了。

轮到我了，我深吸了一口气，身子往后仰，腿越来越弯，已经钻了一半了！我继续往后仰……

低　　　　　更低　　　　　最低

啪！
我都快哭出来了。
我站起来走到一边。
南希和卢克跟着我。

　　"高个子一点儿都不好。"我抱怨着。

　　"你说得不对。"卢克说,"在游行队伍里,你能看到每个人的头顶!"

　　"你还能够到放在架子最上面的饼干!"南希说。

　　"就算是吧。"虽然我嘴上这样说,可心里还是闷闷不乐。

"我知道怎么能让你开心。"卢克说,"明天是体育日。你不是最喜欢体育日了嘛!"

　　没错,我是很喜欢,不过那是以前了。我以前还喜欢跳绳和钻竹竿呢!

　　可现在,我是高个子缇娜了。

体育日的活动一早就开始了。卡莫老师把我和南希、卢克分到橙色队。嗯，也许没那么糟糕。

"第一项,爬杆。"卡莫老师说,"爬得最高的同学将为他的队赢得1分!"

哎呀!爬杆可不是我的拿手项目。

21

　　轮到我了。我吸了一口气，抓住铁杆，使劲一蹿，爬呀爬呀。

　　"时间到！"卡莫老师喊。

　　我低头一看，没爬多高嘛！不过，至少也没掉下来。

　　"绿色队得 1 分。"卡莫老师宣布。

| 高 | 更高 | 最高 |

下一个比赛项目叫迈大步。我对战绿色队的安娜和麦克。大家先热了热身。

"以最少步数到达红线的同学赢1分。"卡莫老师向我们解释了比赛规则。"各就各位,预备——开始!"

我使劲迈出一大步,然后换腿,又是一大步,就这样一直到了终点。

大　　　　更大　　　　最大

　　"安娜用了 10 步,麦克用了 9 步,缇娜用了 8 步。"卡莫老师宣布,"就是说……"

　　我屏着呼吸。

　　"橙色队得 1 分!"

　　我们整个队伍都欢呼起来。南希和卢克的喊声最大。

最后一个比赛项目是跳远。各队的比分好接近哪！"跳得最远的那个队获胜。"卡莫老师说。

卢克先跳。他跳得很远！

然后是麦克。他跳得更远了。

绿色队目前领先。我最后上场。

我深吸了一口气，助跑，闭眼……

跳！

　　双脚落地。哎,我跳到哪儿了?太紧张了,我都不敢睁眼看。

　　"漂亮!缇娜!"只听见我的队友们大喊。

　　我睁开一只眼睛瞄了瞄。哈!我成功了!我跳得最远!

远　　　　　更远　　　　　最远

“橙色队获胜！”卡莫老师宣布。

太出乎意料了！我只知道站在沙坑里，傻乎乎地笑。

卡莫老师颁给我一枚蓝色奖章。

好事真是接二连三。
星期四，我发现了一根长
跳绳，红色的手柄闪闪发
光。我用起来正合适！

麦克的足球卡到了
树枝上。同学们都试着
去够，但只有我的长胳
膊派上了用场。

"谢啦！大个儿！哦，不对，我是说
小巨人缇娜！"麦克笑嘻嘻地说。

　　"缇娜，我要任命你为咱们班的特别助理，专门负责够东西！"李老师说。

　　南希和卢克都冲我竖起了大拇指。

星期五终于到了,要拍集体照啦!

你们猜怎么着?我站在最后一排,而且一点儿也不介意了!

高个子的好处

- 能迈出很大很大的步子
- 跳远比谁都远
- 总能看到别人的头顶
- 能够到别人够不到的东西
- 坐在教室最后面
- 集体照的时候最显眼

没错，那个小巨人就是我——缇娜！

量的比较

你可以用词语来描述每行的 3 幅图。

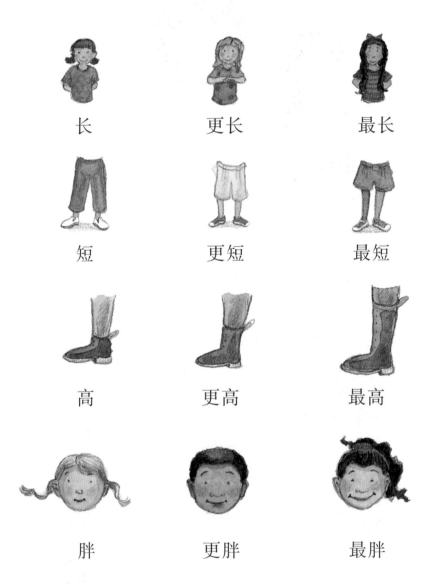

长　　　　更长　　　　最长

短　　　　更短　　　　最短

高　　　　更高　　　　最高

胖　　　　更胖　　　　最胖

亲爱的家长朋友，请您和孩子一起完成下面这些内容，会有更大的收获哟！

提高阅读能力

- 请孩子看看封面上的书名。和他聊一聊，从书名可以知道缇娜是个什么样的孩子？
- 和孩子一起读这个故事。然后，请孩子在书里找出所有比缇娜矮的人和东西。再找一找，有没有什么人或者什么东西比缇娜还要高？
- 在故事的开头，缇娜比好朋友个子高了，她是怎么想的？长高以后，有什么事做起来没有从前那样灵活了？又有什么事做起来更简单了？到了故事结尾，缇娜的心情有了什么样的转变？为什么呢？

巩固数学概念

- 请看第 5 页。谁最高？谁最矮？
- 请孩子找到缇娜想要南希跟她一样高的那一页，再找到缇娜想跟卢克一样矮的那一页。缇娜的方案为什么没有成功？和孩子一起讨论，能不能把一件东西变得和另一件东西一样高？动手试试看。

● 请看第 16 页。孩子们玩钻竹竿的游戏时，竹竿的高度从低，到更低，再到最低。请和孩子一起玩钻竹竿的游戏，让孩子尝试一下这三种情况。

● 第 23 页的图中，孩子们迈出的步子大小不一。给孩子几根不同长度的毛线，请孩子找一找长毛线，更长的毛线和最长的毛线。还可以请孩子按照"一大步—更大一步—最大一步——小步—更小一步—最小一步"的顺序玩一玩迈大步。

生活中的数学

● 请再读第 7 页。缇娜为什么不能再用那根紫色的跳绳了？问问孩子，有没有过因为个子长高了而不能再用心爱的东西的经历？想想看，在生活中有哪些解决方法，或者有哪些方法可以帮助你接受这样的变化。

● 找一些朋友或者家人，让孩子给他们按照个子高矮排排队（或者给高度不同的物品排排队）。先从矮到高，然后从高到矮，再按"高矮高矮"的顺序。有没有哪些人或者东西是一样高的？

● 为孩子制作成长图表，记录下孩子的年龄和身高。在每个记号旁边记录下孩子最喜欢的游戏活动。当孩子长高长大以后，这些喜好会有什么变化吗？

3 只杂技团的猴子想比一比轻重。它们挂在相同的 3 根弹簧下面。图中是它们静止后的样子。哪一只最重？哪一只最轻？

4个同样大小的盒子,哪个最重呢?请在最重的盒子下面画"√"。

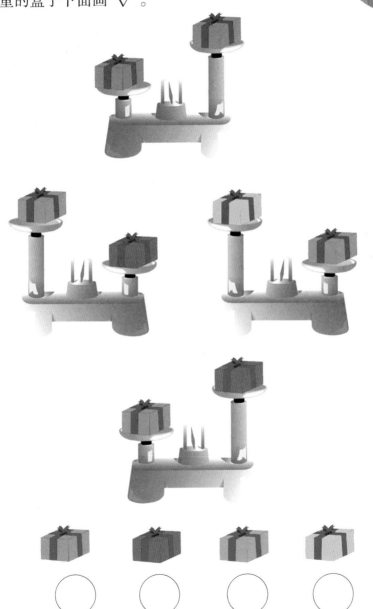

哪根毛线更短呢？动手试一试吧！

哪根晾衣绳更长呢？

1 号运动员和 2 号运动员,你认为谁骑得更快?

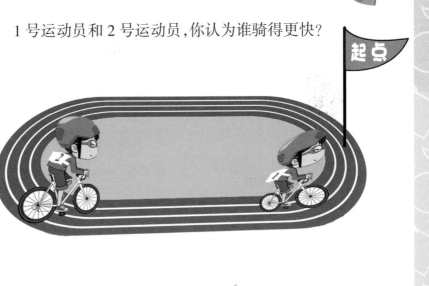

起点

1 号运动员骑了 5 圈。

2 号运动员骑了 5 圈半。

看！缇娜和朋友们在用竹竿测水深。请你加入进来，想一想，水池和小河比，哪儿的水更深呢？

照片中，为什么缇娜、南希和卢克看起来一样高呢？秘密就藏在下面的 3 堆砖块里！你知道拍照时他们脚下各有几块砖吗？请将头像和他们脚下踩的砖块对应地连起来吧！

互动练习 1：
左起第 1 只猴子最重，第 2 只猴子最轻。

互动练习 2：
篮球架离缇娜最远。

互动练习 3：
蓝色盒子最重。

互动练习 4：
(1)直的毛线更短。
(2)晾晒了 5 件衣服的绳子更长。

互动练习 5：
2 号运动员骑得更快。

互动练习 6：
水池中的水更深。

互动练习 7：

（习题设计：何　晨）

42

TOO-TALL TINA

Something happened to me this summer.

I grew. I grew taller and taller and taller!

I went to see Dr. Tasso for my checkup. "Wow, Tina! " she said. "That's some growth spurt you've had! "

I felt proud!

But on the first day of school, I stop feeling so great.

I used to be as tall as my two best friends. Now I'm taller than Nancy. I'm taller than Luke. I'm the tallest kid in third grade!

I say hi to Mike.

"Hi, Tina! " he says. Then he looks up at me. "Whoa, I mean—Too-Tall Tina! "

"How's the weather up there? " Anna asks.

Mike and Anna laugh.

I don't think they're very funny.

At recess I find my favorite jump rope from last year. It's purple with sparkly handles. I take a big jump, and—Crash! My favorite jump rope is too short for me.

Maybe Mike is right. Maybe I am Too-Tall Tina.

Nancy and Luke help me up.

"Thanks," I mumble.

"Don't worry," Luke says. "You just need a longer rope! "

I try to smile.

43

It's almost time to go home.

"Don't forget, Friday is Class Picture Day,"Mr. Lee reminds us. "Let's make our class look sharp."

All the kids are excited—except me.

The lady who takes our picture always lines us up by how tall we are. Nancy and Luke and I are next to each other every year.

But not this year.

"I don't want to be in the back row, away from you guys," I moan.

"Maybe you'll like the back row." says Nancy.

"Yeah! When you're in the back, no one can tell if your socks are dirty! " Luke adds.

"But we're always together—like the Three Musketeers," I reply.

Nancy and Luke shrug sadly.

That night I get to thinking.

Aha! I know what to do. I go to my closet, and...Yes! These are perfect! Nancy and Luke will be as tall as I am on Picture Day.

Before school starts, I tell Luke and Nancy my idea.

"Girls' shoes? "Luke gasps. "No way! "

"Oooh! High heels," says Nancy. She puts them on and starts to walk. Wobble, wobble— Plop! She falls, and lands with a thud.

So much for Plan One.

It's time for Plan Two.

I tuck my head in. I bend my knees. I squish myself down and waddle over to Luke.

"Now I'm as short as you are! " I tell him.

"Yeah," Luke says. "But you look like a duck."

That's not good. I stand back up.

"Hey, guys! " calls Felix. "Want to play limbo? "

"All right! " Nancy and Luke yell. They rush over. I follow—slowly.

Last year I was super at limbo. I'd scoot right under the stick—even when it was really, really low.

But now I'm Too—Tall Tina.

When my turn comes, I take a deep breath. I bend my knees lower and lower. I lean back farther and farther. I'm half way under the stick! I lean back just a little more—

Splat!

I feel like crying.

I get up and walk away.

Nancy and Luke follow me.

"There's nothing good about being tall, "I complain.

"That's not true," Luke says. "You can see over everybody's head at parades! "

"And reach the cookies on the top shelf! " adds Nancy.

"I guess so," I say. But I still feel bad.

"I know what will cheer you up," Luke says. "Tomorrow is Sports Day. You love Sports Day! "

I do love Sports Day. Well, I used to love it—just like I used to love jumping rope and playing limbo.

But now I'm Too—Tall Tina.

Sports Day starts first thing in the morning. Our gym teacher, Ms. Como, puts me on the Orange Team with Nancy and Luke. Hmm. Maybe this won't be so bad after all.

"The pole climb is first," Ms. Como says. "Whoever climbs the highest gets a point for his or her team! "

Uh—oh! I'm not so great at pole climbing.

It's my turn. I gulp hard, grab the pole, and pull myself up. I pull and pull.

"Time's up! " Ms. Como calls out.

I look down. I didn't get very far. Oh, well. At least I didn't fall off the pole!

"That's one point for the Green Team," says Ms. Como.

The next game is Giant Steps. It's me against Anna and Mike. We warm up.

"Whoever reaches the red line in the fewest number of steps wins a point," Ms. Como explains. "Ready, set—Go! "

I stretch my legs as far as I can and take a long step. Then I take another and another—all the way to the finish line.

"Anna took ten steps, Mike took nine, and Tina took eight," Ms. Como says. "That means..."

I hold my breath.

"The Orange Team gets a point! "

My whole team starts to cheer. Nancy and Luke cheer the loudest.

Our last game is the long jump. The score is tied. "The team that makes the longest long jump wins," says Ms. Como.

Luke goes first. He jumps far!

Then it's Mike's turn. He jumps farther.

The Green Team is in the lead. And I'm the last one to go.

I take a deep breath. I start to run. I close my eyes.

I jump!

My feet hit the ground. Where did I land? I'm too nervous to look.

"Way to go, Tina! " my team shouts.

I peek out of one eye. I did it! I jumped the farthest of anyone!

"The Orange Team wins! " Ms. Como announces.

I'm so surprised I just keep standing in the sand pit with a smile on my face.

Ms. Como gives me a big blue ribbon!

More good things happen. On Thursday I find a long jump rope with red sparkly handles. It's perfect!

Then Mike's soccer ball gets stuck in a tree. Lots of kids try to reach it. But only my arms are long enough.

"Thanks, Too-Tall Tina! Er, I mean Terrifically Tall Tina! "Mike says.

"Tina, I'm going to make you our official Class Reacher! " Mr. Lee says.

Nancy and Luke give me a thumbs up.

Finally it's Friday—Class Picture Day!

And guess what? I don't mind being in the back row.

After all, I'm Terrifically Tall Tina!

GOOD THINGS ABOUT BEING TALL
· You can take giant giant steps.
· Your long jumps are very long.
· You can see over everybody's head.
· You can reach stuff nobody else can.
· You get to sit in the back of class.
· You stand out in the class picture!